30 Characteristic Studies
30 charakteristische Etüden
30 Études caractéristiques

Works by / Werke von / Œuvres des
Arban, Concone, Kopprasch, Kreutzer, Sachse, Schmidt

for Trumpet in B♭
für Trompete in B
pour Trompette en si♭

Edited by / Herausgegeben von / Edité par
Michael Schmidt

ED 21277
ISMN 979-0-001-18008-5

www.schott-music.com

Mainz · London · Berlin · Madrid · New York · Paris · Prague · Tokyo · Toronto
© 2014 SCHOTT MUSIC GmbH & Co. KG, Mainz · Printed in Germany

Preface

There are many first-rate exercises available to cover all aspects of trumpet playing. Tried and tested exercises by various authors are brought together here in a selection that includes a few new pieces by the editor, too.

These exercises vary in difficulty, but are generally aimed at advanced pupils still at school or students starting at music college. Emphasis is placed on tone quality, slurring, rhythmic accuracy and technique.

In order to combat the negative image unjustifiably associated with studies, this selection focuses on pieces that display a musical quality likely to inspire players. This will increase motivation - and practice becomes more effective when it is fun.

Some of these pieces are definitely suitable for inclusion in a concert program. The exercises do not have to be played in the order in which they are printed, though the first four pieces are particularly suitable for warming up. It is best to choose a study that fits in well with the rest of your current practice material.

Enjoy your practice!

Michael Schmidt
Translation Julia Rushworth

Working with these studies

These studies focus on various different points, though most provide practice in several areas. Here are a few tips to help you find what you are looking for more quickly:

Warming up
Like athletes, instrumentalists also have to prepare their bodies for the levels of performance their music making requires (strength, stamina, flexibility etc.). This is particularly true of trumpeters, who also require strength, stamina and flexibility besides other musical skills. Preparation should therefore involve not only the muscles required for lip control and breathing, but the whole body. Warm-up exercises provide an opportunity to concentrate individually on posture, embouchure and breathing and on achieving a balance between these.
The following exercises are particularly suitable for warming up: No. 1, No. 2, No. 9

Playing slurred notes
The following exercises are chiefly designed to maintain flexibility in the lips. Some of them are also useful for warming up.
No. 3, No. 6, No. 7, No. 8, No. 10, No. 17, No. 20, No. 23

Technique
By technique I mean both speed and accuracy with the right hand (operating valves) and accurate sounding of notes. This calls for good hearing, correct breathing, powerful attack and flexible embouchure, together with quickness of mind. All these abilities need to be perfected and combined.
These exercises should be useful here: No. 7, No. 15, No. 19, No. 20, No. 21, No. 22, No. 23, No. 25

Articulation
With these exercises be careful to observe articulation markings closely. Ornaments are included, too.
No. 2, No. 8, No. 12, No.14, No. 16, No. 22, No. 23, No. 24, No. 25, No. 26, No. 27, No. 28, No. 30

Rhythm
While some other exercises include rhythmic challenges, the emphasis here is on syncopation, uneven time signatures and changes of time.
No. 11, No. 18, No. 29, No. 30

Musical expression/shaping
Almost all the pieces in this collection can be shaped musically in a variety of ways. Markings (accents, slurs etc.) are to be understood as suggestions: you may adapt these to suit your own taste. The following studies have a distinctive character, however, and thus provide a particular challenge:
No. 2, No. 4, No. 5, No. 6, No. 9, No. 13, No. 14, No. 19, No. 22, No. 24, No. 26, No. 28

Vorwort

Es gibt inzwischen hervorragende Übungen für den Trompeter, die alle Bereiche abdecken. Darum sind hier Übungen von verschiedenen Autoren zusammengetragen worden, die sich in der Praxis bereits bewährt haben. Der Herausgeber hat die Auswahl durch eigene neue Stücke ergänzt.
Die Übungen sind von unterschiedlicher Schwierigkeit und richten sich in der Regel aber an den fortgeschrittenen Schüler bzw. Studienanfänger. Viel Gewicht wurde auf Tonqualität, Bindungen, Rhythmus und Technik gelegt.
Um dem negativen Image, das Etüden teilweise haben, entgegenzuwirken, wurden vorwiegend solche ausgewählt bzw. geschrieben, die eine gewisse musikalische Qualität besitzen und zur Interpretation anregen. Dadurch wird die Motivation erhöht: Spaß beim Üben steigert den Effekt.
Einige Stücke eignen sich durchaus auch für einen Programmpunkt in einem Konzert. Die Übungen müssen nicht in der gedruckten Reihenfolge gespielt werden, obwohl sich die ersten vier Stücke besonders zum Einblasen eignen. Am besten sucht man die Etüde heraus, die gerade eine sinnvolle Ergänzung zum Übematerial darstellt.

Viel Spaß und Erfolg beim Üben!

Michael Schmidt

zur Arbeit mit den Etüden

Die Etüden haben verschiedene Schwerpunkte. Die meisten sind aber geeignet, um mehrere Bereiche zu üben. Damit Sie schneller finden was Sie suchen, hier einige Hinweise:

Zum Einblasen
Wie Sportler sollten auch Instrumentalisten ihren Körper gut vorbereiten, um auch die geforderte Leistung (Kraft, Ausdauer, Lockerheit usw.), die sie für das Musizieren brauchen, abrufen zu können. Dies gilt besonders für die Trompeter und Trompeterinnen, die neben den musikalischen Fähigkeiten auch Kraft, Ausdauer und Flexibilität benötigen. In die Vorbereitung sollte daher nicht nur die Lippen- und Atmungsmuskulatur einbezogen werden, sondern der gesamte Körper. Bei den Aufwärmübungen hat man die Gelegenheit, sich auf die einzelnen Komponenten wie Körper, Ansatz und Atmung zu konzentrieren und auf deren Ausgeglichenheit zu achten.
Folgende Übungen sind besonders für das Einblasen geeignet: No. 1, No. 2, No. 9

Die Bindungen
Zur Erhaltung der Flexibilität der Lippen sind in erster Linie folgenden Übungen gedacht. Sie eignen sich zum Teil auch zum Einblasen.
Übungen: No. 3, No. 6, No. 7, No. 8, No. 10, No. 17, No. 20, No. 23

Die Technik

Unter Technik verstehe ich zum einen die Fertigkeit der rechten Hand (Betätigung der Ventile), und zum anderen die Treffsicherheit der Töne. Hierfür sind natürlich ein gutes Gehör, die richtige Atmung, ein kraftvoller und flexibler Ansatz, sowie schnelle Auffassungsgabe notwendig. Alle diese Fähigkeiten müssen vervollkommnet und kombiniert werden.
Dazu sollen diese Übungen dienen: No. 7, No. 15, No. 19, No. 20, No. 21, No. 22, No. 23, No. 25

Die Artikulation

Bei diesen Übungen ist darauf zu achten, dass die Artikulationsbezeichnungen genau auszuführen sind. Auch die Verzierungen zählen dazu.
No. 2, No. 8, No. 12, No.14, No. 16, No. 22, No. 23, No. 24, No. 25, No. 26, No. 27, No. 28, No. 30

Der Rhythmus

Zwar sind auch in manch anderer Übung rhythmische Nüsse zu knacken, in diesem Kapitel wird aber der Schwerpunkt auf Synkopen, ungerade Taktarten und Taktwechsel gelegt.
No. 11, No. 18, No. 29, No. 30

Musikalischer Ausdruck/Gestaltung

Fast alle Stücke dieser Sammlung lassen sich musikalisch abwechslungsreich gestalten.
Die Vorgaben (Akzente, Bindungen usw.) sind als Anregungen zu verstehen. Sie können alles Ihrem Geschmack anpassen. Die folgenden Etüden verfügen aber über einen eigenen Charakter und bieten dadurch eine besondere Herausforderung:
No. 2, No. 4, No. 5, No. 6, No. 9, No. 13, No. 14, No. 19, No. 22, No. 24, No. 26, No. 28

Préface

Il existe aujourd'hui d'excellentes études pour la trompette qui couvrent tous les domaines. Nous en avons donc réuni ici un certain nombre de différents auteurs – autant de pages qui ont fait leur preuve dans la pratique. À ce florilège, nous avons ajouté de nouveaux morceaux de notre plume.

Si les études de ce recueil présentent divers degrés de difficulté, elles conviennent généralement à des élèves avancés ou à ceux qui se lancent dans une formation de trompettiste. L'accent a été mis sur la qualité de la sonorité, les liaisons, le rythme et la technique.

Pour effacer l'image négative qui affecte à tort l'étude, nous avons choisi ou écrit des morceaux qui ont une certaine qualité musicale et encouragent le trompettiste à faire de la musique. On augmente ainsi la motivation : le fait de prendre du plaisir en travaillant sa technique permet d'aboutir à un meilleur résultat.

Certaines études peuvent très bien être inscrites à un programme de concert. Elles ne doivent pas nécessairement être jouées dans l'ordre du recueil, même si les quatre premières sont idéales pour s'échauffer. Le mieux est de choisir celles qui complètent de manière sensée le programme de travail que l'on s'est fixé.

Puissent ces études procurer du plaisir et mener au succès !

Michael Schmidt
Traduction Daniel Fesquet

Travailler les Études

Les études de ce recueil sont généralement centrées sur une difficulté particulière. Toutefois, la plupart permettent de travailler différents aspects techniques. Nous avons classé ci-dessous ces divers aspects afin de permettre au trompettiste de trouver plus facilement ce qu'il recherche.

Échauffement

Comme les sportifs, les instrumentistes ont intérêt à bien préparer leur corps pour pouvoir recourir aux ressources physiques nécessaires pour faire de la musique. Ceci vaut tout particulièrement pour les trompettistes qui ont besoin, outre d'aptitudes musicales, de puissance, d'endurance et de souplesse. L'échauffement ne doit par conséquent pas seulement concerner les muscles des lèvres et de la respiration, mais tout le corps.
Les études centrées sur l'échauffement permettent de travailler certaines composantes comme l'aspect corporel, l'attaque et la respiration, et de veiller à ce qu'elles soient harmonieuses.
Les études suivantes sont particulièrement bonnes pour l'échauffement : No 1, No 2, No 9

Les liaisons

Les études suivantes, qui permettent aussi en partie de s'échauffer, ont été retenues pour travailler la souplesse des lèvres :
No 3, No 6, No 7, No 8, No 10, No 17, No 20, No 23

La technique

Par technique j'entends d'une part l'agilité de la main droite (l'actionnement des pistons), d'autre part la sûreté d'attaque des sons. Celle-ci nécessite une bonne oreille, une bonne respiration, une attaque puissante et souple, ainsi qu'une vive capacité de réaction. Chacune de ces aptitudes doit être perfectionnée et associée aux autres.
Les études suivantes sont destinées à ce travail : No 7, No 15, No 19, No 20, No 21, No 22, No 23, No 25

L'articulation

Dans les études suivantes, on veillera à respecter soigneusement l'articulation indiquée ainsi que l'ornementation :
No 2, No 8, No 12, No 14, No 16, No 22, No 23, No 24, No 25, No 26, No 27, No 28, No 30

Le rythme

Même si l'on trouvera des difficultés rythmiques dans bien d'autres études, le rythme est ici le sujet principal, plus précisément les syncopes, les mesures non binaires et les changements de mesure.
No 11, No 18, No 29, No 30

Musicalité / Interprétation

Presque tous les morceaux de ce recueil se prêtent à une interprétation musicale différenciée. Les études indiquées ci-dessous ont cependant un caractère bien marqué et représente ainsi un défi particulier. Les indications (accents, liaisons, etc.) sont à prendre comme des suggestions, et le trompettiste pourra les adapter à son goût.
No 2, No 4, No 5, No 6, No 9, No 13, No 14, No 19, No 22, No 24, No 26, No 28

Contents / Inhalt / Contenu

Waltz
Walzer / Valse

Michael Uwe Schmidt
*1943

© 2014 Schott Music GmbH & Co. KG, Mainz

54 669

Adagio

Conradin Keutzer
1780 – 1849

54 669

Slurs
Bindungen / Liaisons No.1

Michael Uwe Schmidt
*1943

Elegy
Elegie / Élégie

Michael Uwe Schmidt
*1943
(nach Concone)

54 669

Monolog
Monologue

Michael Uwe Schmidt
*1943

54 669

Wash of Waves
Wellenschlag / Choc des Vagues

Giuseppe Concone
1801 – 1861

54 669

Triolissimo

Ernst Sachse
1813 – 1870

54 669

16

Slurs
Bindungen / Liaisons No.2
Pentatonic Scale / Pentatonik / Gamme pentatonique

Michael Uwe Schmidt
*1943

Waltz
Walzer / Valse No.2

Giuseppe Concone
1801 – 1861

Slurs
Bindungen / Liaisons No.3

Ernst Sachse
1813 – 1870

Synkopen
Syncopes

Giuseppe Concone
1801 – 1861

Allegretto grazioso

D.C. al Fine

Swing in

Michael Uwe Schmidt
*1943

Einsam
Lonely / Solitaire

Michael Uwe Schmidt

Melody
Melodie / Mélodie

Giuseppe Concone
1801 – 1861

54 669

Forefinger Blues
Zeigefinger-Blues / Blues de l'index

Michael Uwe Schmidt
*1943

Bolero

Michael Uwe Schmidt

Runing

Michael Uwe Schmidt
*1943

Tricky
Verzwickt / Compliqué

Michael Uwe Schmidt
*1943

Hesitatingly
Zögernd / En hésitant

Ernst Sachse
1813 – 1870

54 669

Middle finger-dance
Mittelfingertanz / Danse du majeur

Michael Uwe Schmidt
*1943

Study
Etüde / Étude
No. 1

Jean-Baptiste Arban
1825 – 1889

Allegretto

21

Fancy Bits
Schnörkeleien / Fioritures

Georg Kopprasch
1800?

54 669

Study
Etüde / Étude
No. 2

Jean-Baptiste Arban
1825 – 1889

Allegro moderato

Humoreske
Humoresque

Ernst Sachse
1813 – 1870

Andante

24

54 669

Study
Etüde / Étude
No. 3

Jean-Baptiste Arban
1825 – 1889

D.C. al Fine

Call and Response
Frage und Antwort / Appel et réponse

Georg Kopprasch
1800?

1.) Played
Ausführung

Schaumburg Dance
Schaumburger Tanz / Danse de Schaumburg

Trad./ Michael Uwe Schmidt
*1943

Fine

D.C. al Fine

54 669

Progress
Fortschritt / Progrès

Giuseppe Concone
1810 – 1861
arr. Michael Uwe Schmidt

54 669

Beating Time
Taktieren / Battre la mesure

Michael Uwe Schmidt
*1943

À la Jazz

Michael Uwe Schmidt
*1943